Hello Friends!

Places I Know

Imagine That!

Oh, What Fun!

Let's Go Outside

What a Funny Animal!

IMAGINATION
An Odyssey Through Language

Hello Friends!

Gail Heald-Taylor
General Consultant, Language Arts

HARCOURT BRACE JOVANOVICH, PUBLISHERS
Orlando San Diego Chicago Dallas

Printed in the United States of America

ISBN 0-15-332802-9

Acknowledgments

For permission to reprint copyrighted material, grateful acknowledgment is made to the following sources:

Harper & Row, Publishers, Inc.: From *Bear By Himself* by Geoffrey Hayes. Copyright © 1976 by Geoffrey Hayes. "Very Tall Mouse and Very Short Mouse" from *Mouse Tales,* written and illustrated by Arnold Lobel. Copyright © 1972 by Arnold Lobel.

Lothrop, Lee & Shepard Books, a division of William Morrow & Company, Inc.: Silly Goose by Jan Ormerod. Copyright © 1986 by Jan Ormerod.

Pantheon Books, a division of Random House, Inc.: From *Goodbye, Hello* by Robert Welber. Copyright © 1974 by Robert Welber.

Art Credits

Chuck Bowden: 41 (adapted from a photograph, Thomas Wommack, courtesy Harper & Row); June Goldsborough: 2-11; Geoffrey Hayes: 42-62; Arnold Lobel: 34-40; Karen Loccisano: 16, 17; Jan Ormerod: 18-33.

Cover: Tom Vroman

Photo Credits: The Terry Wild Studio: 12-15

Contents

Hello Friends!

Places I Know

Imagine That!

Oh, What Fun!

Let's Go Outside

What a Funny Animal!

From Good-bye, Hello

A story in verse by Robert Welber

Pictures by June Goldsborough

A kitten goes creeping
Away from the rug.

Good-bye, Mother.
Hello, bug.

A mouse goes out
To climb and see.

Good-bye, Mother.
Hello, tree.

A bird begins
To try to fly.

Good-bye, Mother.
Hello, sky.

A squirrel comes running
Down the tree.

Good-bye, Mother.
Hello, bee.

A child is watching
Each little creature.

Good-bye, Mother.
Hello, teacher.

Connections

Birthday Fun

Story Time at School

Silly Goose

A story by Jan Ormerod

I hop
like a flea.

I jump
like a kangaroo.

I paddle
like a duck.

I flap
like a bat.

I parade
like a peacock.

I hide my head
like an ostrich.

Look at me!

My Mom says . . .

sometimes I'm just
as silly as a goose.

Very Tall Mouse and Very Short Mouse

Story and pictures by Arnold Lobel

Once there was a very tall mouse
and a very short mouse
who were good friends.

When they met
Very Tall Mouse would say,
"Hello, Very Short Mouse."
And Very Short Mouse would say,
"Hello, Very Tall Mouse."

The two friends would often
take walks together.

As they walked along
Very Tall Mouse would say,
“Hello, birds.”

And Very Short Mouse would say,
“Hello, bugs.”

When they
passed by a garden,
Very Tall Mouse would say,
"Hello, flowers."

And Very Short Mouse
would say,
"Hello, roots."

When they passed by a house,
Very Tall Mouse would say,
“Hello, roof.”

And Very Short Mouse
would say,
“Hello, cellar.”

One day the two mice
were caught in a storm.

Very Tall Mouse said,
"Hello, raindrops."

And Very Short Mouse said,
"Hello, puddles."

They ran indoors to get dry.

"Hello, ceiling,"
said Very Tall Mouse.

"Hello, floor,"
said Very Short Mouse.

Soon the storm was over.

The two friends
ran to the window.

Very Tall Mouse held
Very Short Mouse up to see.

"Hello, rainbow!"
they both said together.

About
ARNOLD LOBEL

When he was seven years old, Arnold Lobel began telling stories. First he made up stories for his friends at school. Then he made up stories for his own children when they were small. Arnold Lobel was an author and illustrator of books. Many children enjoy his stories and drawings.

Arnold Lobel said, "When I write my stories, I always sit in the same chair. I do my writing in the late afternoon. That is a good time to think about frogs and toads and mice and crickets."

More Books by Arnold Lobel

Mouse Tales
Frog and Toad Together
Days with Frog and Toad
Owl at Home
Fables

Bear by Himself

From a story by Geoffrey Hayes

There are times when a bear
has to be alone with himself,

to think his own thoughts

and sing his own songs.

He must pause and enjoy:
listening to the quiet,

smelling the rain

or talking to a river.

He likes to watch the wind
in the high trees,

sail his kite—alone and free—

or do nothing at all!

He lies in the thick grass with the sun hot on his fur and remembers:

misty dim mornings

and cool winter breezes,

warm little rooms where the fire
pleases.

He has a secret place
where no one can find him

and worlds to explore
in his own backyard.

As the evening deepens to darkness,

there is his own friendly house
to come home to

with his books and his toys
and his own soft bed.

He feels the dark
and sleeps—
and dreams.

8
C 9
D 0
E 1
F 2
G 3
H 4
I 5
J 6